Mac 2016

Cartoons from the *Daily Mail*

Stan McMurtry **mac**

dp

DELANCEY
PRESS

For my wonderful, brave and beautiful wife, Liz.

First published in the United Kingdom in 2016 by Delancey Press Ltd.
23 Berkeley Square, London W1J 6HE
www.delanceypress.co.uk
Copyright © Stan McMurtry, 2016
The moral rights of the author have been asserted.

Typeset by ForDesign
Printed and bound by TJ International Ltd.

ISBN: 9781907205446
To order visit: www.delanceypress.co.uk

Looking back it is hard for me to believe that I have been drawing for the *Daily Mail* for forty six years. I was taken on by the paper for a trial period and I still haven't been told that I've got the job.

It has all been and continues to be great fun and has given me the opportunity to meet so many fascinating people. I was once sent to a nudist colony, asked to strip off and hand over a drawing to two naked ladies. I have been invited to Downing Street, been on Desert Island Discs, been sworn at by politicians, met a few prime ministers and been presented with an MBE by Her Majesty the Queen.

I really enjoy the daily challenge of dreaming up a few ideas on the day's news and drawing them to the best of my ability.

Here is a selection of this year's mind wanderings. I hope you will like them.

Patron: Frederick Forsyth CBE

Founding Patron: Dame Beryl Bainbridge DBE

mac 2016 – Winter collection www.peoplesbookprize.com

1 December 2016 – 28 February 2017

THE PEOPLE'S
BOOK
PRIZE™

Foreword

Mac's wonderful cartoons should be, must be, the first port of call for any sane *Daily Mail* reader. Day after day, indeed year after year, he brightens the morning with wit and superb draughtsmanship, sometimes making a serious point, sometimes an hilarious one, often both at once. You don't have to believe me, but after you've taken even the briefest look at the wonderful artistry reproduced herein, you will.

Tim Rice

'Not now, Donald!'

'To be honest, love, it was a bit of a surprise for me too. All I did was clean his shoes.'

'Hard feelings? Good heavens, no! We're inviting all Labour and
Lib Dem peers to a party here on November the fifth.'

'Nein, nein. Not your credit card. Haf you got a British NHS European Health Insurance Card?'

'Not only e-cigs. The NHS is helping with my addiction to whisky and wild, wild women.'

'Dear Jermain Defoe. I have been doing all those tasks on your list for 35 years, FREE! ... Call me.'

'You will meet a group of military types bearing an enormous rocket which they will place firmly up your trousers...'

'Well honestly. The NHS pays for a fun packed, health giving holiday and all you can do is moan!'

'Exciting news, Gerald – our Veronica has had a marriage proposal!'

'You've picked up your grandson's phone again. That "send naked photo" text was for him!'

'Did you hear that? ... The sat-nav said: "Ve verr only obeying orders".'

'No, don't wake him. Tell him in the morning that a wealth distribution team was here.'

'... so I said, "Don't worry, Jeremy. For a few quid I'll press your button for you" ... He said he'd let me know.'

'It must have happened just after you said, "Let's get building!".'

'Well honestly. We put a 5p charge on plastic bags and still they come!'

'Honestly, darling. When I said I felt an overwhelming urge to "come out" – I meant of the EU!'

'I'm back, love. Three wasted years, and for all we know Assange could've slipped out of the embassy months ago!'

'Hey, great idea, man. Nice fur. How many of you guys are in there?'

'You know what to do, Simpkins – saunter casually past
and check what the lying scumbag's got in his tin mug'

'Honestly. Directions to the gents would have been enough, Mr Cameron.'

'I told you not to have that extra sausage!'

'Any more thoughts on tax credit cuts, George?'

"NO IFS, NO BUTS MERKEL. THESE ARE MY DEMANDS!...ER,...IF THEY'RE ALL RIGHT WITH YOU"

"DAMN!"

"GOODNESS GRACIOUS! ALL THREE OF YOU SPEAK ENGLISH – HOW UNUSUAL IN THIS COUNTRY."

'I've got to visit the ladies' room. I'll be about four hours.'

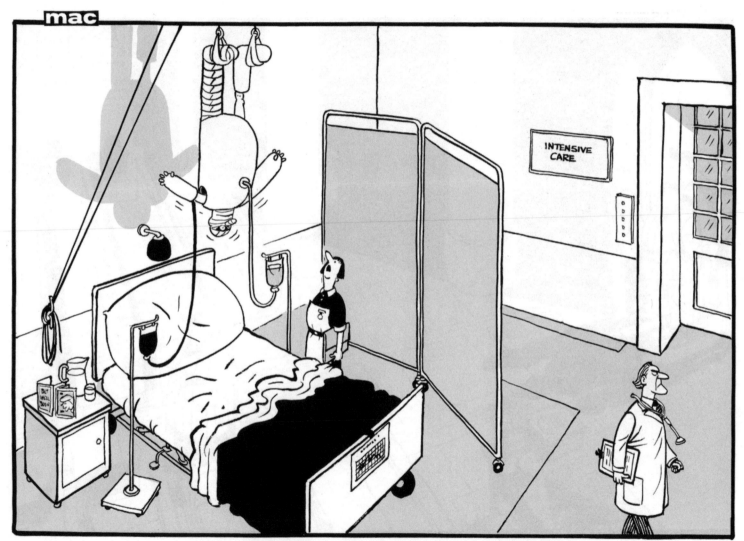

'I take it the doctor's heard your views on striking?'

'Psst. Is this the place where you can hear offensive prayers what's been banned in the cinemas?'

'Can you hurry up with the new submarines? We can't keep calling the AA out!'

'Fantastic news! You can now buy this desirable bijou residence under the new affordable homes scheme.'

'Well he was David Cameron just before he stood up'

'We're terribly sorry. There's been an unfortunate test tube
mix-up with the IVF puppy research lab down the road'

'Apparently he's in Brussels, Your Royal Highness, but promises whatever happens you'll be the first to know.'

'WOWEE, Sharon! Did the earth move for you too?'

'We three kings of Orient are. Bearing gifts we've travelled so far ...'

'For goodness' sake! That Indian lad who scored a record 1009 runs not out didn't keep whining "Please Daddy can I go to bed now?"'

'Yes, dear. I think your peppermints are working. I haven't even thought of a drink for two days.'

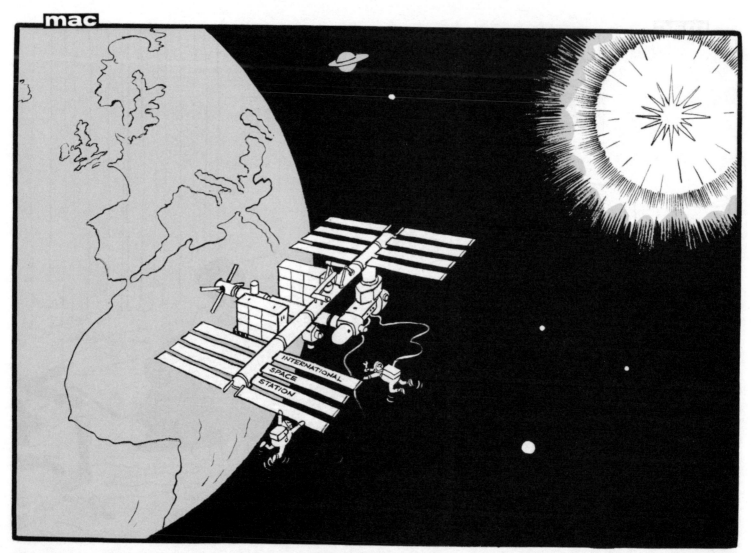

'Ground control to Major Tim – a huge unidentified star has suddenly appeared – please investigate'

'You weren't needed, chum. Our plumber did the operation. I'm just checking with you that he got the right bit.'

'Good evening. I'm your husband's boss. Poor you. I happen to know he's spending the night with Gloria from sales and marketing.'

'We've got the test results, Mrs Wilkins. Unfortunately your husband is a bit like Trident would be under Jeremy Corbyn'

'What do you think, Donald. Should women living in the UK wear burkas?'

'Fluffy...Fluffykins!...Now where has that dog got to?'

'Great show. How did you manage to smuggle the gunpowder into Jeremy Hunt's basement?'

'Personally, headmistress, I think we could make an exception in the case of Mrs Merrihew.'

'Top of the mornin' to you. I'm absolutely banjaxed!... I thought I was coming here for a rest!'

'Hello. GM labs? This time we'd like to hear the pitter-patter of a tiny cordon bleu cook...'

'All right, Mr Assange. You can stay a bit longer, but as you're now officially dead, Lord Lucan – you can hop it!'

'Oh, do stop moaning, Wayne – at least you're home during the week now.'

'This lady from Cornwall says can she have her shed back – it's got her husband in it'

'Now, what was it you asked for just before our strike? Ah yes, a bedpan.'

'We deserve it. Organising cuts for everyone else is absolutely exhausting.'

'Scaremongering? Who, moi?'

'Here comes your blind date now... check him out, Sharon. He doesn't look like the Pope to me.'

'I assure you, William is not backing the EU. All members of the royal household are completely unbiased.'

'COME ON. YOU'RE NEARLY THERE!'

'Good evening, sir. Mr Cameron sends his compliments and hopes that on
June 23rd he can count on your support...'

'Amazing isn't it? I wasn't aware of this either.'

'Y'know, Mum and Dad. Cameron can get things wrong. It's possible the world won't come to an end on June 23rd.'

'Okay. There are side effects. But look, darling – not one grey hair!'

'Well my mum doesn't think tackling should be allowed – so she lent me her Taser'

'Don't deny being a Brexit supporter, Mrs Perkins. The listening device in your mop transmits straight to Downing Street!'

'We're ruined! Maria Sharapova has been banned for four years!'

'So many bare chested hunks on TV nowadays – shame Nigel Farage never takes his shirt off'

'Hang on. You didn't book Matt LeBlanc when he was doing wheel spins!'

'I said: Do you remember when it was plastic bags?'

'You heard me. Get rid of them. The client wants Theresa May!'

'If that bloke Novak Djokovic is right, what're we doin' wrong?'

'Yes, love. We got a phone call from your lorry. 26 chicken sandwiches, 12 teas, 14 coffees, no sugar.'

'Good evening, Madam. I believe you rang for the Night Manager ...'

'All is not lost. It seems there really is such a thing as reincarnation.'

Mac's tribute to his friend Ronnie

THE Mail's legendary cartoonist Mac — a long-time admirer, friend and one-time golfing partner of Ronnie Corbett — was moved yesterday to draw this special appreciation

'I'd like to save the industry, chaps. But I just don't know where to find the money.'

'Yes. Can you come quickly, officer? My wife's been listening to the Archers!'

'Look, they've printed my advert – "I will hide your wealth, secure cellar, no questions asked …"'

'David. There's a gentleman from the Inland Revenue to see you . . . David?'

'Mr Cameron will be pleased. So many volunteers to deliver his pro Europe leaflets.'

'The restaurant, Gerald. Where you got food poisoning ... did you leave a tip?'

'What's going on? We've spent ages getting here on the bus and Donald Trump isn't even on the list'

'I'm sorry, Godfrey. They've recounted the votes six times and you still only got one.'

'Pah! You don't scare me, Cameron. I'm still voting Brexit.'

'... So I said, "I want to get out of Europe" ... "Oh really?" says Dave. "Have a drink"...
It had a funny taste...'

'I assure you, ambassador. My wife meant no offence to you slitty-eyed people.'

'...so I said: 'Honestly, all this fuss just because I left a fake bomb in the stadium by mistake. It was only a silly game of football.'

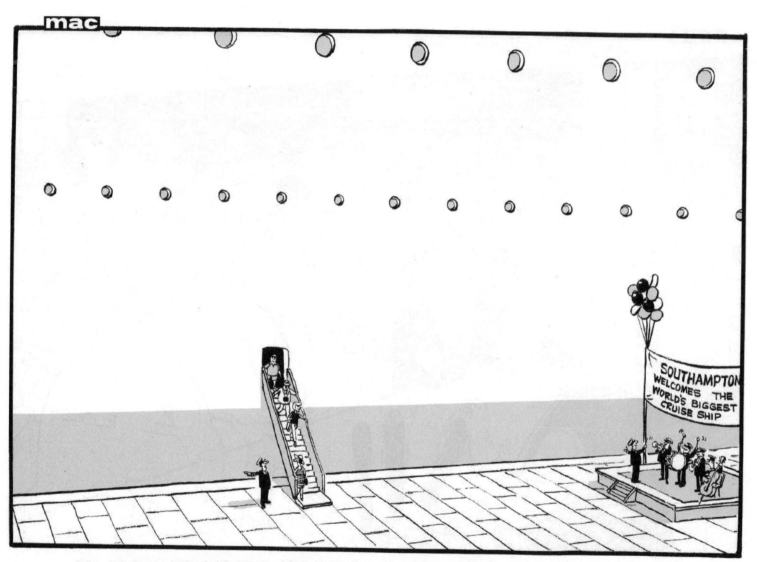

'No, Madam. This is Southampton. You wanted Portsmouth where the front end is.'

'I'm just popping out m'dear. Is there anything you want in Australia?'

'Good decision, old chap. Everyone's entitled to a bit of privacy.'

'Andrew. Your father and I would like a word!'

'Cameron must be getting desperate. Is he going to do that to all Brexit supporters?'

'Spending your bank 'oliday in France, eh? Ooh 'ow I love to talk to 'andsome Eenglish men...'

'He's cheaper than most people smugglers – just a donation for his church roof.'

'Neighbourhood Watch, Skegness branch reporting, Home Secretary...
all quiet...request short bathroom break...over.'

'Stone me! The Brexit Poms want to take up our pints system – they won't regret it.'

'... so that's some nice French wine, Camembert, Calvados,
Dijon mustard ... oh, and don't forget the 20 Albanians'

'I think we're getting somewhere. He had a sudden urge to nip out for a few pints followed by a curry.'

'Yes, it's a Banksy but with a few additions by Davey!'

'I expect there are millions of keen young people like our Wayne still too busy to register for a vote.'

'Let's hope a whole three weeks watching footy isn't going to be spoilt by any violence!'

'... and here comes Brexit, over the massive fence, then the barbed wire, past the pit of snakes ... just George Osborne's landmines to go ...'

'Certainly, sir. Which Brexit rally would you like Mr Geldof to make obscene gestures and shout abuse at?'

'He wants eleven people to remain in Europe and the other sixty-four million to leave.'

'It's crunch day, Philip. The nation decides who's in charge – me or Mrs Merkel.'

'Game, set and match...but wait...the losers are asking for the result to be looked at again...'

'Taraaa! Your problems are over!'

'Bad news, Mangler. He got away with it.'

'Yes, go on, Margaret... Buy a really big handbag... Then what?'

'It's so unfair. There's no mention of all I DID achieve!'

'Remember this is only until you find the keys to your new place'

'There she goes... One unarmed torpedo, round the coast, down the Thames, into the drains, then straight up Jeremy Corbyn's lavatory.'

'Olga, the high jump's over there. That's for the pole vault'

'I 'ope the speeches aren't too long. I've still got Cameron's carpets to 'oover.'

'Tell them to stop whinging and wear dark glasses – heck I wear them all the time.'

'You're a taxpayer, sir. Which one do you think is robbing you blind?'

Sketches that have not been published

" . . . So after much scientific study I conclude all drinks should be made legal and that you Miss Spilsbury are absolutely gorgeous."

"Beats me why they'd want to come here knowing what happens at Christmas."

"She's quite a feminist - asked me if I'd like to be Chancellor of the Exchequer."

"Four new Tridents? Yeah, Okay. When do you want them by?"

"If I've got this book of useful phrases right he's saying we've got the wrong seats."

"Here's a bickie for the bestest doggie in the world before we do nice walkies."